Advances in Science
Learning from the Past,
Looking to the Future

私たちと科学の世界
過去から未来へ

Dave Rear
Kayoko Murakami

NAN' UN-DO

Advances in Science
Learning from the Past, Looking to the Future

Download Audio

音声ファイル
無料 DL
のご案内

このテキストの音声を無料で視聴（ストリーミング）・ダウンロード
できます。自習用音声としてご活用ください。
以下のサイトにアクセスしてテキスト番号で検索してください。

https://nanun-do.com 　テキスト番号 [**512023**]

※ 無線 LAN（WiFi）に接続してのご利用を推奨いたします。

※ 音声ダウンロードは Zip ファイルでの提供になります。
　お使いの機器によっては別途ソフトウェア（アプリケーション）
　の導入が必要となります。

To Teachers and Students

Sometimes we need to look backwards in order to look forward. That is to say, in order to understand the world of science today and where it may be heading tomorrow, it helps to know where it has been in the past. How did we come to our present understanding of atoms, energy, gravity and light? What are the fundamental principles through which we investigate the world around us? Who are the great scientific figures who helped us to find our place in the universe? This book aims to answer these questions, guiding students from the past to the present and from the present to the future.

It is divided into five main sections, each with three units that illustrate the major theme. The first section deals with the fundamentals of science, showing how we learned to investigate the universe through the scientific method and read it in the language of mathematics. In the second section, we see how some of the great scientific thinkers of history built upon these fundamental principles to make stunning discoveries about the nature of light, electricity, radiation and the human body. In the third section, we look beyond our own world into the vastness of space. We learn about the mysteries of gravity and atoms and discuss the possibility that human beings will one day leave our solar system and travel to distant space. The final two sections of the book connect our present understanding of science with the future of technology. We look at nanotechnology, genetic engineering and artificial intelligence, and ask how such advances will change our world and, just as importantly, whether these changes will all be to our benefit.

To guide students through the topics introduced in the book, each unit has a number of different activities for them to complete. They consist of two vocabulary exercises, one pre-reading and the other post-reading, which give practice in using the key terms introduced in the article. There are also two comprehension activities, the first a reading exercise based on true / false questions and the second a listening exercise in which students predict the answer and check it with the audio. Following this is a grammar activity which helps students to increase the complexity and accuracy of their sentence building, and a technical exercise introducing language commonly used in the scientific world, from formulas, shapes and dimensions to graphs, directions and equipment. The unit ends with a pair of discussion questions which encourage students to use their own experiences and opinions to think beyond the topic. Thank you for taking an interest in this book. I hope you enjoy using it!

Dave Rear

Table of Contents

Unit 1: The Scientific Method

The scientific method is the basis for how experiments are carried out and new scientific discoveries are made. But what are the steps involved in the method? And who were the first scientists to start using it?

Key Vocabulary

Match the following words with their meaning.

1. theory   (a) to carry out, perform

2. conduct   (b) to stress the importance of something

3. observation   (c) a quality or characteristic

4. emphasize   (d) an idea that aims to explain something

5. property   (e) the act of watching something carefully

If you have ever carried out an experiment at school or university, you have probably followed some version of the scientific method. The scientific method consists of a series of steps that should be completed in order to test a particular theory or make a new scientific discovery. Briefly put, these steps are as follows: First, ask a question about something you have observed: how, why, what, etc. Second, conduct background research to gain more information about the topic to which the question relates. Third, based on this background research, construct a hypothesis, which is an educated guess about what the answer to your question might be. Fourth, design and perform an experiment in order to test your hypothesis. Fifth, carefully record the results of your experiment and analyze the data you have collected. Finally, conclude whether to accept or reject your hypothesis and communicate your findings in the form of a report or presentation.

Nowadays the scientific method is one of the fundamental principles through which we attempt to increase our understanding of the world around us. But it was not always the case. Although some ancient Greek philosophers advocated the use of systematic observation in order to draw up theories about the natural world, the scientific method as we know it today is generally traced back to the work of scholars such as Francis Bacon and Galileo Galilei. Francis Bacon was born in England in 1561 and educated at Cambridge University, where he became critical of the methods used to teach science. Emphasizing a methodical and skeptical approach to knowledge, Bacon insisted on the use of artificial experiments to verify conclusions about the natural world. Although the precise methods employed by Bacon differ from those used in science today, his so-called 'empirical' approach was the foundation upon which the modern scientific method was built.

Bacon's work was the inspiration for other scientists of his age, such as Isaac Newton and Galileo Galilei. Both of these great thinkers combined an empirical approach with a deep understanding of the importance of mathematics. Galileo conducted a large number of experiments during his illustrious career, with one famous, if unproven, story saying that he once dropped two balls of different weights from the Leaning Tower of Pisa in order to prove that an object will fall to the ground at the same speed, regardless of its mass. Newton, meanwhile, discovered, amongst many other things, the properties of light by refracting white light through a prism in order to split it into the colors of the rainbow.

Bacon, Newton and Galileo have been called the 'fathers of modern science.' The empirical methods they pioneered still form the basis for how new discoveries are made today.

(l. 7) hypothesis 仮説　　(l. 12) principle 原理　　(l. 14) advocate ～を主張する
(l. 16) scholar 学者　　(l. 18) skeptical 懐疑的な　　(l. 19) verify ～を検証する，証明する
(l. 26) illustrious 輝かしい　　(l. 29) refract ～を屈折させる

Reading Comprehension

Decide if the following statements are true (T) or false (F).

1. (   ) In the scientific method, the hypothesis is constructed after conducting background research.

2. (   ) An experiment must always prove the hypothesis is correct.

3. (   ) The scientific method used today is usually traced back to Greek philosophers.

4. (   ) It was Francis Bacon who first advocated an empirical approach to scientific discovery.

5. (   ) Newton showed that white light is made up of different colors.

Listening Comprehension

Predict the correct questions for the answers below. Then check your responses with the audio.

1. _____

   There are six of them.

2. _____

   That objects will fall to the ground at the same speed.

3. _____

   Because they advocated the empirical methods that are used in modern science.

Words in Science

Choose the correct word for each sentence from the list below.

1. Antoine Lavoisier was a famous _____ in the fields of chemistry and biology.

2. Through the experiment, the researchers' _____ was proved to be correct.

3. A ray of light will _____ when it passes through glass.

4. Hopefully we will able to _____ our conclusion when we analyze the data.

5. The technology behind these devices is all based on the same _____ .

> hypothesis   principle   scholar   verify   refract

Understanding Technical Language – Formulas I

Following the example given, complete the exercise below.

Ex: $a(b+c) = ab \times ac$ a open brackets b plus c close brackets equals ab times ac

Ex: $A = \dfrac{dy}{dx}$ Capital A equals dy over dx

1. x plus y equals a over b _____

2. x open brackets 8 minus a close brackets equals y _____

3. Capital m equals a plus b all over c _____

4. $\dfrac{a}{b} \times \dfrac{c}{d} = \dfrac{ac}{bd}$ _____

5. $A = R\left(1 + \dfrac{r}{n}\right)$ _____

Building Sentences – Active and Passive Verbs

Following the example given, rewrite the sentences below.

Ex: [Active]   The scientists *used* the scientific method in the experiment.

     [Passive]   The scientific method *was used* in the experiment (by the scientists).

1. [Active]   The researchers *passed* an electric current through the liquid.

   [Passive]   _____

2. [Active]   The scientist *mixed* oxygen with hydrogen to produce water.

   [Passive]   _____

3. [Passive]   A model *was created* by the engineers as a first step.

   [Active]   _____

Discussion

Talk about these questions with your classmates.

1. When did you become interested in science? Why does science interest you?

2. Have you ever carried out an experiment in school or university? Did you follow the scientific method described in the passage?

Unit 2: Observing the Solar System

It was not until the 17th century that we began to understand the Earth's position within the solar system. The discovery that the Earth revolves around the Sun, rather than the other way around, was a hugely important moment in science. Why is this?

Key Vocabulary

Match the following words with their meaning.

1. assume   (a) to move or revolve around something, like a planet around the Sun

2. orbit   (b) to investigate a place or topic you do not know much about

3. propose   (c) to believe something is true, even without proof

4. precise   (d) exact and accurate

5. explore   (e) to suggest an idea or plan

As far back as our history stretches, human beings have gazed up towards the heavens and wondered about the thousands of tiny, shining objects that light up the night sky. Nowadays we are all familiar with the idea that the Earth is part of a system of eight planets, or nine if we include Pluto, that continually revolve around the Sun at the center. But this
5 understanding of the solar system, and our place within it, was not widely accepted until the late 17th century. Before that, it was assumed that it was not the Earth that orbited the Sun, but the Sun that orbited the Earth. The Earth, at the center of the solar system, and indeed the universe, was stationary, and all the other objects in the night sky moved around it.

Although a Greek philosopher named Aristarchus of Samos proposed the idea of a
10 heliocentric, rather than a geocentric, model of the solar system as early as the 3rd century BC, the first explanation based on mathematics was not made until Nicolaus Copernicus published his famous work *On the Revolutions of the Celestial Spheres* in 1543. Copernicus's conclusion—'We revolve around the Sun like any other planet'—was hugely controversial at the time, since it contradicted the official teaching of the dominant Catholic Church. Some
15 scholars, however, were inspired to investigate further. In 1610, Galileo Galilei, who made one of the world's first telescopes, observed that Jupiter had four moons which revolved around it, proving that not all heavenly bodies orbited the Earth. He also made observations of Venus and of the Sun itself which were not consistent with the geocentric model of the universe. At around the same time, the German mathematician Johannes Kepler precisely described the
20 orbits of the known planets and formulated laws that explained their movement.

By the end of the 17th century, the heliocentric model of the solar system had been accepted, marking an important moment in history in which scientific observation prevailed over religious belief. As our ability to explore our solar system has progressed, many more important discoveries have been made. As well as the first landing on the moon made by the
25 crew of Apollo 11 in 1969, spacecraft have been sent out to photograph the outer planets, bringing us spectacular photographs of Jupiter, Saturn, Uranus and Neptune. The spacecraft Voyager 2, which was launched in 1977, is still flying today and has now passed beyond our solar system into interstellar space. Japan too is involved in space exploration. In 2018, the spacecraft Hayabusa2 successfully landed on the asteroid Ryugu, collecting samples of its
30 surface that could advance our knowledge of the solar system even further.

(l. 1) gaze ～を見上げる　　(l. 8) stationary 動かない，固定された　　(l. 10) heliocentric 太陽中心の
(l. 10) geocentric 地球中心の　　(l. 10) model モデル　　(l. 13) controversial 議論を引き起こす，
物議を醸している　　(l. 14) contradict ～と矛盾する，相反する　　(l. 14) dominant 支配力を持つ，有力な
(l. 18) consistent with ～と一致する，調和する　　(l. 22-23) prevail over ～より優先する　　(l. 28)
interstellar 星間の　　(l. 29) asteroid 小惑星

Reading Comprehension

Decide if the following statements are true (T) or false (F).

1. (   ) Until the late 17th century, it was not believed by many people that the Earth revolved around the Sun.

2. (   ) Nicolaus Copernicus was the first person to suggest the heliocentric model of the solar system.

3. (   ) The Catholic Church supported the geocentric model of the solar system.

4. (   ) Galileo supported Copernicus's model using observations he made with a telescope.

5. (   ) The spacecraft Voyager 2 is currently flying within our solar system.

Listening Comprehension

Predict the correct questions for the answers below. Then check your responses with the audio.

1. _____

   There are nine if we include Pluto.

2. _____

   Galileo Galilei and Johannes Kepler.

3. _____

   It successfully landed on the asteroid Ryugu.

Words in Science

Choose the correct word for each sentence from the list below.

1. Copernicus challenged the _____ view that the Earth was at the center of the solar system.

2. Having disproved the old theory, the physicists created a new _____ for how the universe works.

3. Since our results were _____ with previous studies on this topic, we believe they are accurate.

4. A _____ idea is one that creates a lot of disagreement or debate.

5. We did not expect our study to _____ the findings of other scholars in this field.

> model   controversial   contradict   dominant   consistent

Understanding Technical Language – Formulas II

Following the example given, complete the exercise below.

Ex: $a^2 + b^3 = c^n$ *a* squared plus *b* cubed equals *c* to the power of *n*

Ex: $\sqrt{x} \times \sqrt[3]{y} = A^{n-1}$ The square root of *x* times the cube root of *y* equals capital *a* to the power of *n* minus 1

1. *a* to the power of *n* plus the square root of *b* equals *c*   _____

2. *x* squared over *y* cubed equals capital *m* to the power of 10   _____

3. The square root of open brackets *a* squared minus *b* squared close brackets

                                         _____

4. $\sqrt[3]{a - b} = \frac{x}{y}$ _____

5. $C = a^{n-1} \times \sqrt{b}$ _____

Building Sentences – Verbs with to~ and ~ing

Put the words in the correct order and rewrite the sentences below.

Ex: Galileo was (of / inspired / to / ideas / the / investigate) Copernicus.

     Galileo was *inspired to investigate the ideas of* Copernicus.

1. We must (mistake / the / making / same / avoid / as) last time.

     _____

2. The student (to / time / managed / assignment / her / on / finish).

     _____

3. This (tends / down / to / whenever / break / machine) we use it for too long.

     _____

Discussion

Talk about these questions with your classmates.

1. Are you interested in studying about space? What things about space interest you the most?

2. Do you think it is a good idea for Japan to spend a lot of money on space projects like Hayabusa2? Are the benefits of space exploration worth the high cost?

Unit 3: The Beauty of Mathematics

Love it or hate it, mathematics is fundamental to almost every kind of science and has been an important part of learning for thousands of years. Some people also say it is beautiful in the same way as art or music. What do you think?

Key Vocabulary

Match the following words with their meaning.

1. fundamental

2. multiplication

3. division

4. geometry

5. sequence

(a) a type of mathematics that deals with lines, angles and shapes

(b) a sum such as $30 \div 6$

(c) important, central

(d) a series of events or numbers in a certain order

(e) a sum such as 9×6

The word 'mathematics' comes from the ancient Greek word *mathematikos*, meaning 'fond of learning.' This might not be the feeling everybody has toward the subject, but it hints at how fundamental the study of numbers, shapes and patterns is to science and to the world in general. As Galileo said, the universe 'is written in mathematical language' and it 'cannot be read until we have learned the language.'

Not surprisingly then, the study of math is almost as old as learning itself. As early as 3000 BC, the ancient Babylonians were making multiplication and division tables and calculating squares, cubes and fractions. They employed a system based on the number 60 (rather than 10, as today), and it is because of this that we still measure 60 seconds in a minute, 60 minutes in an hour and 360 degrees in a circle. The ancient Chinese, Indians and Greeks also developed advanced mathematical methods, including algebra and geometry, and it is often difficult to know who actually made some of the most famous discoveries. For example, we are all taught in school that the Greek philosopher Pythagoras came up with the well-known theorem about right-angled triangles: $a^2 + b^2 = c^2$. In fact, however, the Babylonians and Indians had been using it centuries before the Greeks.

The number system that most countries use today, the decimal system, was invented by Indian mathematicians around 1,800 years ago. It was not used in Europe until the 13th century, having been spread by Arab traders. The person who popularized the system in the West was a talented Italian mathematician named Fibonacci. He is most famous nowadays for the Fibonacci sequence, in which each number is the sum of the two preceding ones (0, 1, 1, 2, 3, 5, 8, 13, 21 etc.). The Fibonacci sequence is closely related to the so-called 'golden ratio,' a representation of symmetry which has been very influential in design and art. One of the most celebrated architects of the 20th century, Le Corbusier, famously based many of his buildings on the golden ratio, including the National Museum of Western Art in Ueno Park, Tokyo.

The Fibonacci sequence, then, is connected with ideas of beauty. People who genuinely love math often say they find the subject beautiful, comparing it to an art form like music or poetry. In a recent research study, professional mathematicians were shown a series of equations, some of which are often considered as 'beautiful' and some of which are not. The researchers found that when the mathematicians looked at the beautiful equations, they activated the emotional parts of their brains that are normally used when viewing works of art. As for the most beautiful equation of all, the mathematicians chose one called Euler's identity, which looks like this: $e^{i\pi} + 1 = 0$. What do you think? Better than the Mona Lisa?

(l. 8) fraction 分数　　(l. 11) algebra 代数　　(l. 13) Pythagoras ピタゴラス（ギリシャの哲学者）　　(l. 14) theorem 定理, 法則　　(l. 16) decimal 10進法の　　(l. 22) symmetry 対称性　　(l. 24) National Museum of Western Art 国立西洋美術館　　(l. 31) activate 〜を活性化させる, 稼働させる

Reading Comprehension

Decide if the following statements are true (T) or false (F).

1. (   ) Galileo invented the use of mathematics for reading the universe.
2. (   ) Thanks to the ancient Babylonians, we still use the number 60 as a base for measuring time.
3. (   ) Pythagoras was the first person to understand the mathematical relationship between the sides of a right-angled triangle.
4. (   ) The design of the National Museum of Western Art in Tokyo can be connected to the Fibonacci sequence.
5. (   ) Recent research shows that the brains of mathematicians react to beautiful equations in the same way they react to works of art.

Listening Comprehension

Predict the correct questions for the answers below. Then check your responses with the audio.

1. _____

   It meant 'fond of learning.'

2. _____

   An Italian mathematician called Fibonacci.

3. _____

   The equation known as Euler's identity.

Words in Science

Choose the correct word for each sentence from the list below.

1. If we convert 25 percent into a _____ , the answer will be $\frac{1}{4}$.
2. Pythagoras's _____ is related to right-angled triangles.
3. Of all the types of mathematics, _____ is my least favorite.
4. By turning this dial, we can _____ the robot's legs.
5. The _____ system is used by most countries today.

algebra   activate   fraction   theorem   decimal

Understanding Technical Language – Formulas III

Using the symbols in the box, complete the following exercise.

±	≠	∞	<	∴	>	∝	°C	≈	≥

1. Therefore x equals y _____

2. 100 degrees Celsius _____

3. x does not equal 0 _____

4. x is greater than 10 _____

5. Infinity _____

6. x is greater than or equal to 10 _____

7. a is approximately equal to b _____

8. x equals plus or minus 5 _____

9. x is proportional to y _____

10. x is less than 10 _____

Building Sentences – Which and Who

Following the example given, rewrite the sentences below.

Ex: I bought a new computer. It had much more memory than the old one.

I bought a new computer *which* had much more memory than the old one.

1. Fibonacci was a mathematician. He lived during the 13th century.

_____

2. Hayabusa2 is a spacecraft. It landed on the asteroid Ryugu.

_____

3. Please do not forget the assignment. You were given it last week.

_____

Discussion

Talk about these questions with your classmates.

1. Do you enjoy art forms such as music, art, poetry, photography, filmmaking and design? Which art form are you most interested in?

2. How do you feel about mathematics? Do you think it can be beautiful?

Unit 4: From Light Bulbs to LEDs

The invention of the light bulb in 1879 helped to bring about the modern age, in which electricity powers almost everything in our homes. We owe our convenient lifestyles to the work of figures like Volta, Faraday and Edison. What exactly did they do?

Key Vocabulary

Match the following words with their meaning.

1. appliance
2. manage (to)
3. soak (in)
4. optical
5. transform

(a) to deal with something successfully

(b) to place in a liquid for a length of time

(c) relating to light

(d) to change something completely

(e) a household good that uses electricity

Imagine a world without electricity. A world without appliances like light bulbs, refrigerators, microwaves, heaters, televisions or computers. For many people, this is, sadly, not difficult to imagine at all since around 1.2 billion human beings, 15 percent of the global population, do not have access to power. For those of us fortunate enough to have been born in developed
5 countries, however, life without electricity seems almost inconceivable. But if we could travel back in time to just 100 years ago, we would find that this was the world in which everybody lived, no matter how rich or poor. How did we manage to achieve our present mastery of electric power?

Most people are aware that the electric light bulb was invented in 1879 by Thomas
10 Edison, one of America's greatest ever innovators. But Edison did not create the light bulb out of thin air. Several other scientists, including Alessandro Volta and Michael Faraday, had already conducted experiments with electricity and gradually begun to uncover its secrets. Volta is regarded as the inventor of the first electric battery in 1799, when he placed together disks of zinc and copper (the electrodes) separated by cardboard soaked in salt water (the
15 electrolyte). His invention showed that electricity could be generated chemically, rather than simply existing in nature, and opened the door to a new world of advances. In 1821, the English scientist Michael Faraday built on the discovery of electromagnetism to design the first electric dynamo, which soon led to the production of electric motors. Encouragingly for some of us, Faraday was not good at mathematics, and the equations that describe the laws
20 for electric, optical and radio technologies were drawn up later by James Clerk Maxwell.

The electrical devices that power the world today are based on the work done by these men of the 18th and 19th centuries. Though they have become much more efficient and varied, modern batteries still work on the same chemical principle discovered by Volta. As for the light bulb, Edison's invention provided the basis for a century of electric light that
25 transformed homes and streets all over the world. It was only recently that a new type of bulb came into widespread use: the LED bulb. Far more efficient than the old kind, LEDs (light-emitting diodes) rely on semiconductors that light up when an electric current flows through them. At first, they could only produce red and green light, so they could not create the white light needed for bulbs. That problem was solved by the invention of blue light LEDs by
30 Japanese researchers Professors Akasaki, Amano and Nakamura. In 2014, the trio were awarded the Nobel Prize in physics for their work.

(l. 5) inconceivable 想像を超えた，信じられない　(l. 11) out of thin air どこからともなく，何の根拠
もなく　(l. 14) zinc 亜鉛　(l. 14) copper 銅　(l. 14) electrode 電極　(l. 15) electrolyte
電解液，電解質　(l. 17) electromagnetism 電磁気力，電磁気学　(l. 23) varied 変化に富んだ，多様な
(l. 27) semiconductor 半導体

Reading Comprehension

Decide if the following statements are true (T) or false (F).

1. (　) A century ago, only rich people had access to lots of electrical appliances in their homes.

2. (　) One of Volta's achievements was to show that electricity could be generated rather than simply observed in the natural world.

3. (　) Faraday's invention would not have been possible without the discovery of electromagnetism.

4. (　) Volta's work is not significant when it comes to the principle on which modern batteries are based.

5. (　) White light can be produced by combining red and green LEDs.

Listening Comprehension

9

Predict the correct questions for the answers below. Then check your responses with the audio.

1. _____

   He used zinc and copper.

2. _____

   Because he was not good at mathematics.

3. _____

   Because they invented blue light LEDs.

Words in Science

Choose the correct word for each sentence from the list below.

1. For this experiment, we need a good conductor of heat such as _____ .

2. Modern electronic devices use _____ in their chips.

3. If we attach this _____ here, it should form a circuit.

4. Salt water is an example of a simple _____ .

5. Michael Faraday can be considered one of the fathers of _____ .

> semiconductors　　electrode　　electrolyte　　copper　　electromagnetism

Understanding Technical Language – Shapes

Match the following words with the pictures below.

cube	rectangle	cylinder	cone	hexagon
pyramid	hemisphere	ellipse	sphere	equilateral triangle

1.

2.

3.

4.

5.

_____

6.

7.

8.

9.

10.

_____

Building Sentences – When, Where and Whose

Following the example given, rewrite the sentences below.

Ex: This is a picture of Michael Faraday. His invention led to the first electric motor.

This is a picture of Michael Faraday, *whose* invention led to the first electric motor.

1. Welcome to the laboratory. I conduct my experiments here.

_____

2. Professor Nakamura is a scientist. His work won a Nobel Prize.

_____

3. Volta made the first battery. A door to new advances was opened.

A door to new advances was opened _____

Discussion

Talk about these questions with your classmates.

1. Make a list of appliances you have in your home. How would your daily life be different without them?

2. Nowadays electricity, rather than gasoline, can also be used to power automobiles. What are the advantages and disadvantages of electric cars?

Unit 5: The Risks and Rewards of Radiation

Our mastery of radiation has brought us revolutions in everything from medicine to communication. One of the most famous scientists in history, Marie Curie, helped to unlock the mysteries of this energy. Her work showed us the rewards that could come from using radiation. Unfortunately, it also showed us the risks.

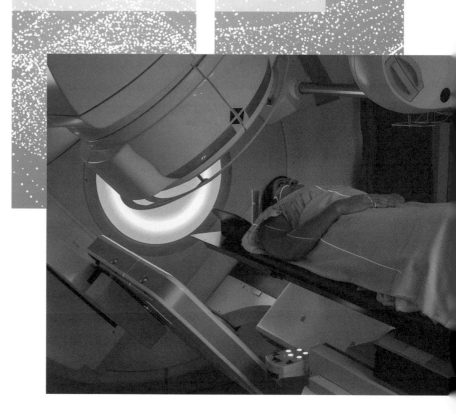

Key Vocabulary

Match the following words with their meaning.

1. particle	(a) to send out gas, heat, light or particles
2. emit	(b) a very small part of an atom
3. radioactive	(c) to think of an idea
4. come up with	(d) to decide what is wrong with someone who is sick
5. diagnose	(e) having or producing energy from radiation

Radiation is energy that moves from one place to another in the form of waves or particles. There are three major types of radiation: electromagnetic radiation, such as infrared, microwaves and X-rays; acoustic radiation, like sound, ultrasound and seismic waves; and particle radiation, which occurs when nuclear particles are emitted from radioactive materials like uranium.

5 Electromagnetic radiation was discovered in the early 19th century. Infrared and ultraviolet were discovered in sunlight by William Herschel and Johann Ritter respectively, while the first radio waves were produced artificially by Heinrich Hertz, whose name is now used as the unit of frequency. In 1895, the German scientist Wilhelm Röntgen detected X-rays. While Röntgen is the name given to these rays in many languages, Röntgen himself called them X-rays after the 10 mathematical term ('x') for something unknown. While investigating the ability of certain materials to stop the rays, he brought a sheet of lead into position and saw an image of his own skeleton for the first time. Two weeks later, he took the very first picture using X-rays of his wife's hand, causing her to exclaim in shock: "I have seen my death!"

Particle radiation was discovered by Henri Becquerel and his brilliant student Marie Curie 15 in 1896. It was Curie who came up with the term 'radioactivity' and revealed many of its secrets. By conducting experiments with the radioactive material uranium, she hypothesized that the radiation must come from the atom itself, rather than through some kind of chemical reaction. This was an important step towards the knowledge that atoms were not indivisible. She also discovered two new elements, which she called radium and polonium.

20 Marie Curie's work won her Nobel Prizes in both physics and chemistry, and radium began to be used almost immediately in medicine for treating cancer and other diseases. Nowadays radiation has so many applications, there are too many to mention. X-rays, gamma rays and ultrasounds are used for both diagnosing and treating medical conditions. Radio waves are used for communication and microwaves for cooking. Infrared is used for imaging and night vision, 25 while alpha particles are necessary for smoke detectors. Along with all these, radioactive materials are also, of course, indispensable for nuclear power generation.

Unfortunately, there is one more lesson to be learned from Marie Curie and her work with radiation. In 1934, at the age of 66, she died from an illness caused by exposure to too much radiation. She herself had not known about the risks of her work, and in fact it was not until the 30 1940s that the harmful effects of radiation became understood. Our knowledge of radiation has brought us incredible technological advances, but it is an energy that must always be treated with care.

(l. 2) infrared 赤外線　　(l. 3) acoustic 音響の　　(l. 3) ultrasound wave 超音波
(l. 3) seismic wave 地震波　　(l. 4) uranium ウラン　　(l. 8) frequency 周波数　　(l. 11) lead 鉛
(l. 18) indivisible 分割できない　　(l. 22) gamma rays ガンマ線　　(l. 25) alpha particles α粒子
(l. 26) indispensable 不可欠の, なくてはならない　　(l. 28) exposure 被ばく, 暴露

Reading Comprehension

Decide if the following statements are true (T) or false (F).

1. (   ) Electromagnetic radiation was discovered after particle radiation.

2. (   ) Röntgen only realized that he had discovered X-rays after he photographed his wife's hand.

3. (   ) Marie Curie's research helped scientists to understand an important fact about atoms.

4. (   ) Radiation began to be used for medical purposes soon after Marie Curie's discoveries.

5. (   ) All three major types of radiation have applications in the modern world.

Listening Comprehension

11

Predict the correct questions for the answers below. Then check your responses with the audio.

1. _____

   They are included in acoustic radiation.

2. _____

   Because it is used as the unit of frequency.

3. _____

   This fact about radiation was understood in the 1940s.

Words in Science

Choose the correct word for each sentence from the list below.

1. The scientists measured the _____ waves generated by the earthquake.

2. Using the _____ machine, the doctor was able to show the woman the baby inside her.

3. The _____ of electromagnetic waves is measured in Hertz.

4. The type of light known as _____ is invisible without special equipment.

5. The dangers of _____ to too much ultraviolet light are now well known.

> ultrasound   frequency   exposure   seismic   infrared

Understanding Technical Language – Dimensions and Materials

Match the following sentences with the pictures below.

> It is XX in length.   It has a height of XX.   It is XX wide.
> It is XX in diameter.   It has a radius of XX.   It is made of (plastic).

1.

2.

3.

_____   _____   _____

4.

5.

6.

_____   _____   _____

Building Sentences – Describing Effects with Verb~ing

Following the example given, rewrite the sentences below.

Ex: Röntgen took an X-ray picture of his wife's hand. It caused her to exclaim in shock.

Röntgen took an X-ray picture of his wife's hand, *causing* her to exclaim in shock.

1. Marie Curie was exposed to radiation. It led to her death in 1934.

_____

2. There was an explosion in the laboratory. It resulted in a fire.

_____

3. I studied very hard. It helped me to pass the exam.

_____

Discussion

Talk about these questions with your classmates.

1. Have you ever had an X-ray? What other kinds of radiation energy are used in your daily life?

2. Nuclear power has both advantages and disadvantages. Do you think that Japan should use nuclear power to generate electricity?

Unit 6: The Man Who Saved Millions

Edward Jenner's work is said to 'have saved more lives than the work of any other human.' When he lived in the 18th century, the life expectancy for an average person was just 40 years. Nowadays it is twice that. One of the major reasons for this dramatic increase is the research of Dr. Jenner. What exactly did he discover?

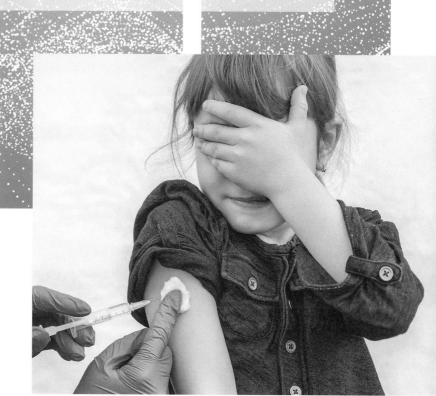

Key Vocabulary

Match the following words with their meaning.

1. life expectancy   (a) an illness that is easily passed from one person to another

2. infectious disease   (b) protected against a particular disease

3. immunity   (c) to destroy or completely get rid of something

4. eradicate   (d) a general development or change in a situation

5. trend   (e) the average age to which a person lives

Perhaps you have never heard the name Edward Jenner, but without him you might never have been born. Why is that? Because Edward Jenner is said to have saved more lives than any person in history; millions, perhaps even billions, all around the world. He was a doctor who lived in England from 1749 to 1823, a time when the life expectancy for a human being

5 was about 40 years, around half that of today. The main reason life expectancy was so low was the high probability of dying from an infectious disease, particularly during childhood.

The biggest killer of all was a disease known as smallpox. Smallpox was a highly infectious virus which caused red spots to break out all over the body, rather like measles. It had existed for centuries all over the world. In 735 AD, for example, it killed 35 percent of

10 the population of Japan, with people believing it had been sent by demons. In Edward Jenner's time, around 10 percent of the population in England died of the disease.

As a doctor, Jenner saw cases of smallpox all the time. He had noticed, however, that people who worked with cows rarely seemed to catch the disease. Jenner hypothesized that the reason was because they were exposed to a cow virus called cowpox, which was similar to smallpox but

15 far less deadly. Jenner deduced that if people could be given a small dose of cowpox, this might make them immune to smallpox. In 1796, he tested his hypothesis on an eight year-old boy named James Phipps, his gardener's son. As expected, the boy developed a slight fever from the cowpox, but did not become seriously ill. When he was exposed to the smallpox virus, he was found to have developed immunity. Over the next few years, Jenner tested more people,

20 including his own 11 month-old son, Robert. All became immune to smallpox.

What Jenner had done was to create the first successful vaccine. Vaccines work by exposing the human body to a harmless version of a particular disease. If a vaccinated person encounters the real disease, their body has already been trained how to fight the infection, allowing it to kill the virus quickly. In the best case scenario, if enough people are vaccinated,

25 this can even lead to the disease itself being eradicated. This is what eventually happened with smallpox. In 1980, after a worldwide vaccination program, the World Health Organization announced that the smallpox virus had been eradicated from the Earth.

Recently, there has been a disturbing trend of people beginning to distrust vaccines. False information is being spread over social media, encouraging people to stop vaccinating

30 themselves or their children. It is an extremely dangerous trend which threatens to facilitate the spread of infectious diseases around the world. As Dr. Jenner showed, vaccines are a powerful weapon against disease. We must never forget their importance.

(l. 6) probability 確率, 可能性　　(l. 7) smallpox 天然痘　　(l. 8) measles はしか, 麻疹　　(l. 15)
deduce 〜を推測する, 推定する　　(l. 15) dose 投与量　　(l. 24) best case scenario 最良のシナリオ
(l. 28) disturbing 動揺させる, 物議をかもす　　(l. 30) facilitate 〜を促進する, 手助けする

Reading Comprehension

Decide if the following statements are true (T) or false (F).

1. ( ) The risk of dying from a disease as a child was a major reason why life expectancy was low in the past.

2. ( ) Jenner realized that it was dangerous for people to work with cows.

3. ( ) Although Jenner's first test was not successful, he tried again until his vaccination method worked.

4. ( ) Vaccination works by making use of the body's natural ability to fight infections.

5. ( ) Recent evidence has shown that vaccination may be dangerous, so we should be careful about using it from now on.

Listening Comprehension

🎧 13

Predict the correct questions for the answers below. Then check your responses with the audio.

1. _____

   No, it had existed for centuries.

2. _____

   It was an eight year-old boy named James Phipps.

3. _____

   That the smallpox virus had been successfully eradicated from the Earth.

Words in Science

Choose the correct word for each sentence from the list below.

1. Schools in the area have been closed due to an outbreak of _____ .

2. From this result we can _____ that the metal is a good conductor of electricity.

3. In the _____ , we should be able to begin producing the new medicine as early as next year.

4. The _____ of catching an infectious disease falls dramatically if most people in an area have been vaccinated.

5. This new robot should _____ our manufacturing process.

| deduce | facilitate | probability | measles | best case scenario |

Understanding Technical Language – Tools and Parts

Match the following words with the pictures below.

screwdriver	spanner	saw	screw	pliers	nail
nut	bolt	cable	plug	socket / outlet	adapter

1.

2.

3.

4.

5.

6.

_____   _____   _____   _____   _____   _____

7.

8.

9.

10.

11.

12.

_____   _____   _____   _____   _____   _____

Building Sentences – Sentences Starting with What

Put the words in the correct order and rewrite the sentences below.

Ex: (done / had / was / what / to / Jenner) create the world's first successful vaccine.

What Jenner had done was to create the world's first successful vaccine.

1. (laboratory / happened / at / what / the / surprised) us all.

_____

2. (aim / I / to / is / do / investigate / to / what) the properties of the material.

_____

3. (the / what / machine / cut / does / is / to / pieces) of metal into the correct size.

_____

Discussion

Talk about these questions with your classmates.

1. Do you usually get the flu vaccination each year?

2. The Australian government has begun to force families to vaccinate their children. What do you think about this policy?

Unit 7: Unlocking the Mysteries of Gravity

When we throw something into the air, we know for certain that it will fall back down. We know also that this is due to gravity. But what exactly is gravity and where does it come from? It is a mystery that has occupied many of the greatest minds in science.

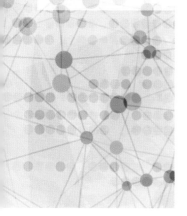

Key Vocabulary

Match the following words with their meaning.

1. gravity   (a) to guess what will happen in the future

2. figure out   (b) the force that pulls objects toward the ground

3. predict   (c) natural events or occurrences

4. phenomena   (d) to be real or present

5. exist   (e) to find the answer, calculate

If there is one thing that everybody in the world knows, it is that if you throw something into the air, it will always come down again, hopefully not on your head. Gravity, of course, is the force that makes this happen. But, considering how fundamental gravity is to our everyday lives, it actually took human beings a long time to figure out that it existed.

5   Isaac Newton was the first scientist to begin to understand gravity after, as the famous story goes, he was sitting in his garden and saw an apple fall from a tree. Since an object cannot suddenly start moving on its own, Newton realized that some kind of force must be acting on the apple to make it fall. From this moment of inspiration, he deduced that the same force must also be acting on the moon to stop it flying away from the Earth into space.

10 Newton called this mysterious force 'gravity' and determined that any object that has mass must also have gravity, with the larger the mass of an object, the greater its gravitational force. Calculating it mathematically, Newton was able to explain the motion and orbits of the planets in our solar system.

There was, however, one planet whose orbit did not quite fit Newton's model, the planet

15 of Mercury closest to the Sun. Scientists puzzled for centuries over why this was, until a brilliant young physicist named Albert Einstein finally figured it out. In his *General Theory of Relativity*, published in 1915, Einstein showed that gravity had the effect of *bending* space and time, and it was this curvature of space that caused objects of less mass to fall toward objects of greater mass. The best way to imagine this is to stretch out a sheet of cloth and then

20 place a metal ball in the center. The ball will bend the sheet, causing any other balls nearby to roll toward it. This is what gravity does to space.

Einstein's theory not only explained the unusual orbit of Mercury but also predicted other strange phenomena in the universe, including black holes and gravitational waves. It was a long time before scientists were able to observe that these phenomena actually existed.

25 Black holes were finally discovered in the 1960s, and it is now believed that all large galaxies, including our own, have a black hole at their center. As for gravitational waves, it was not until 2015 that direct evidence of their existence was observed. Scientists hope that the discovery will bring in a new exciting era of astronomy to help us better understand the universe in which we live.

(l. 8) act on 作用する   (l. 10) determine ～と判断する, 断定する   (l. 12) motion 運動, 動き
(l. 16-17) General Theory of Relativity 一般相対性理論   (l. 18) curvature 屈曲, 曲率
(l. 23) gravitational wave 重力波   (l. 28) astronomy 天文学

Reading Comprehension

Decide if the following statements are true (T) or false (F).

1. (   ) Newton realized that a force must have caused the apple to fall from the tree.

2. (   ) Newton did not figure out that objects of higher mass would have more gravity than objects of less mass.

3. (   ) Newton's theory of gravity explained the orbits of all the known planets in our solar system except one.

4. (   ) Einstein modified Newton's theory by showing that gravity bent space and time.

5. (   ) Observations of black holes and gravitational waves have shown that Einstein's theories were not accurate.

Listening Comprehension

15

Predict the correct questions for the answers below. Then check your responses with the audio.

1. _____

   It was Isaac Newton.

2. _____

   He called it gravity.

3. _____

   Black holes and gravitational waves.

Words in Science

Choose the correct word for each sentence from the list below.

1. The young woman became interested in _____ after she saw a shooting star in the night sky.

2. On Earth, gravity is the _____ that pulls objects towards the ground.

3. Isaac Newton came up with three laws of _____ .

4. The aim of the experiment was to _____ the effects of high temperatures on the new material.

5. Without a force to _____ the apple, it would not have fallen to the ground.

determine	motion	astronomy	force	act on

Understanding Technical Language – Movements and Actions

Match the following words with the pictures below.

| tighten / loosen | rotate | bend | pull | press |
| raise / lower | push | hit | slide | swing |

1. _____

2. _____

3. _____

4. _____

5. _____

6. _____

7. _____

8. _____

9. _____

10. _____

Building Sentences – Cause and Effect

Following the example given, rewrite the sentences below.

Ex: [Cause - Effect] *Since* an object cannot start moving on its own, Newton realized a force must be acting on the apple.

[Effect - Cause] Newton realized a force must be acting on the apple, *since* an object cannot start moving on its own.

1. [Cause - Effect] *As a result of* the study, many new discoveries were made.

   [Effect - Cause] _____

2. [Cause - Effect] *Due to* poor communication, people failed to hear of the problem.

   [Effect - Cause] _____

3. [Effect - Cause] We can leave early *since* our manager gave us permission.

   [Cause - Effect] _____

Discussion

Talk about these questions with your classmates.

1. Have you ever been in an airplane? Where have you been or where would you like to go?

2. What challenges would there be in living in an environment without gravity?

Unit 8: The Strange World of Atoms

Considering that they are the fundamental building blocks of all matter in the universe, atoms are very confusing things. Did you know that you might have a bit of Mozart or Einstein in your body right now? Sounds impossible, but it's true. Let's take a look at the strange world of atoms.

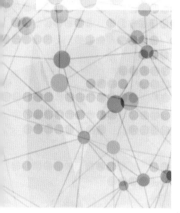

Key Vocabulary

Match the following words with their meaning.

1. aspect
2. organism
3. be comprised of
4. element
5. detect

(a) a chemical substance

(b) part of a situation or subject

(c) to discover something which may be difficult to notice

(d) to consist of, be made of

(e) a living thing, often very small

Many aspects of science can be confusing to those who are not experts, but there is something particularly hard to comprehend about the world of atoms, the building blocks from which all matter is made. First of all, there's the size. Atoms are so tiny that in a single grain of salt, there are estimated to be around 1.2 billion billion of them (or 1.2×10^{18}). Then there's the
5 length of time they survive. Atoms do not die when we do, they simply become part of something else, such as a leaf, a drop of water, or even another human being. Every atom in our bodies has almost certainly passed through several stars and millions of other organisms on its way to us. As many as a billion of the atoms in our bodies could have once belonged to Mozart, Galileo, Einstein or some other famous historical figure. We all like to think we have
10 a genius hidden in us somewhere. Well, it turns out we literally do.

Despite their tiny size, atoms are not the smallest units of matter in the universe. Each atom is made up of even smaller particles inside. In the center is the nucleus, which is comprised of protons and neutrons, and orbiting around that are electrons. In fact, most of the volume of an atom—greater than 99 percent—is just empty space between the nucleus
15 and the electrons. Although some ancient Greek philosophers guessed at the existence of atom-like structures, our knowledge of atoms is usually traced back to the English chemist John Dalton in the early 19th century. From his experiments, Dalton hypothesized that each chemical element had its own atoms that differed from others in mass. Dalton believed that atoms were the smallest unit of matter, but in 1897, J. J. Thomson announced the discovery of
20 the electron. Then, in the early 20th century, Ernest Rutherford and Niels Bohr came up with a new model of the atom, which forms the basis of our understanding today.

Since the work of these pioneers, scientists have extended our knowledge of atomic theory to new levels. Particle accelerators, like the one at the CERN laboratory in Switzerland, have detected new subatomic particles, such as quarks, neutrinos and bosons.
25 Quarks are the smallest known unit of matter, combining to form protons and neutrons; neutrinos have such a small mass that they pass through almost all matter undetected. As for bosons, although there are several kinds, the most famous is the Higgs boson, a particle finally detected at CERN in 2012. Nicknamed the God Particle by the media, the Higgs boson is special because it appears to give all other particles their mass. Without the Higgs boson, in
30 other words, there would be no mass in the universe. Confused? Welcome to the strange world of atoms.

(l. 2) comprehend 理解する　(l. 3) matter 物，物質　(l. 12) nucleus 原子核　(l. 13) proton プロトン，陽子　(l. 13) neutron ニュートロン，中性子　(l. 13) electron エレクトロン，電子　(l. 23) particle accelerator 粒子加速器　(l. 23) CERN 欧州原子核研究機構　(l. 24) quark クォーク (l. 24) neutrino ニュートリノ，中性微子　(l. 24) boson ボソン，ボース粒子

Reading Comprehension

Decide if the following statements are true (T) or false (F).

1. (   ) The atoms in our bodies are not unique to us.
2. (   ) Most of the empty space within an atom is inside the nucleus.
3. (   ) John Dalton did not realize that there were particles which are smaller than an atom.
4. (   ) Quarks are particles that exist inside the nucleus of an atom.
5. (   ) Some scientists believe that the Higgs boson proves the existence of God.

Listening Comprehension

17

Predict the correct questions for the answers below. Then check your responses with the audio.

1. _____

   There are around 1.2 billion billion of them.

2. _____

   Protons, neutrons and electrons.

3. _____

   It was at the CERN laboratory in Switzerland.

Words in Science

Choose the correct word for each sentence from the list below.

1. The theory was so complex, even the professor could not really _____ it.
2. All _____ is comprised of atoms.
3. The CERN laboratory can _____ particles in order to make new discoveries.
4. At the center of an atom is the _____ .
5. Unlike the proton and the neutron, the _____ cannot be found inside the nucleus of an atom.

> accelerate   electron   comprehend   nucleus   matter

Understanding Technical Language – Directions of Movement

Match the following expressions with the pictures below.

to the right	to the left	out of	up and down	across
around	towards	away from	into	through

1. _____

2. _____

3. _____

4. _____

5. _____

6. _____

7. _____

8. _____

9. _____

10. _____

Building Sentences – So ~ that and Such ~ that

Put the words in the correct order and rewrite the sentences below.

Ex: Neutrinos have (they / such / that / a / mass / small / pass) through matter undetected.

Neutrinos have *such a small mass that they pass* through matter undetected.

1. It (successful / was / a / study / she / such / that) was awarded a prize.

_____

2. Atoms (that / so / complicated / we / not / still / do / are) understand them fully.

_____

3. Particles (quickly / move / needed / so / that / equipment / special / is) to detect them.

_____

Discussion

Talk about these questions with your classmates.

1. The atoms in our bodies might have once belonged to a famous person of the past. Which famous people do you most admire and why?

2. The discovery of the Higgs boson was reported in 2012. Do you like to watch the news or read a newspaper? What kind of news are you interested in?

Unit 9: Interstellar Travel

Science fiction movies let us dream of a future in which human beings zoom through space, travelling from one star to another in a matter of hours. There are theoretical ways we might achieve interstellar travel, but is this future ever likely to happen?

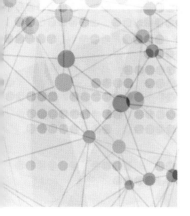

Key Vocabulary

Match the following words with their meaning.

1. comparatively   (a) to meet someone, often unexpectedly

2. encounter   (b) speed

3. expel   (c) relatively, in comparison to other things

4. velocity   (d) to hit something while moving

5. collide (with)   (e) to force gas or liquid out of something

The problem with space is that it's really really big. To travel to Mars, the second nearest planet to Earth, requires a journey of between 56 million and 400 million kilometers, depending on where the two planets are in their respective orbits. Scientists estimate that it would take a manned space flight approximately seven months to travel there with current
5 technology. Interstellar travel refers to a journey to a different solar system, a group of planets that do not orbit around our own Sun. The nearest star to Earth, Alpha Centauri, is 40 trillion kilometers away, around 300,000 times the distance to Mars. The fastest current NASA spacecraft, which cannot carry people, would take 78,000 years to reach it.

Comparatively speaking, Alpha Centauri is close to us; most of the stars we can see in
10 our night sky are much further away than that. In fact, the vast distances between stars is the most likely reason we have never encountered intelligent alien life. For even the most advanced alien civilization, it would simply take too long to reach us. So, what are the chances that human beings will ever be able to travel to different stars or galaxies? The short answer is, not very high. Although there are various theoretical methods by which we might be able to
15 journey to different parts of space, none of them are close to becoming a realistic possibility.

The main idea for achieving interstellar travel involves dramatically increasing the speed at which we travel. Currently, NASA is researching so-called ion engines, which expel charged particles of gas accelerated to a much higher velocity than in a conventional rocket. The problem is that even an ion engine could never produce the velocity necessary for
20 interstellar travel, which would require something close to the speed of light. For that kind of speed, we have to turn to concepts like antimatter engines or laser sails, which are still little more than theoretical ideas. Furthermore, any kind of high-velocity propulsion involves the risk of colliding with a tiny object in space. At such a high speed, even a piece of dust could cause catastrophic damage to a spacecraft.

25 A second idea for achieving interstellar travel involves altering space itself. Einstein's Theory of Relativity predicts the existence of worm holes, which are like tunnels from one part of space to another. No evidence has yet been found of a worm hole, but if they exist—or if we were somehow able to create them—they could provide a shortcut across the galaxy, allowing us to, almost magically, appear in a completely new location. Sadly, the chances of
30 ever being able to use a worm hole like this are almost zero. Science has brought us incredible advances over the past few decades, transforming the way we live our lives. Interstellar travel, however, seems like a jump too far.

(l. 4) manned 有人の　(l. 10) vast 大きな, とてつもない　(l. 14) theoretical 理論上の　(l. 18) charged 荷電した, 帯電した　(l. 21) concept 概念, コンセプト　(l. 21) antimatter 反物質　(l. 22) propulsion 推進力, 稼働力　(l. 24) catastrophic 破壊的な　(l. 25) alter ～を変える

Reading Comprehension

Decide if the following statements are true (T) or false (F).

1. ( ) With current technology, it would take a spacecraft 78,000 years to reach the nearest star.

2. ( ) Even if aliens exist, they are probably too far away from Earth for us to meet them.

3. ( ) Ion engines might be able to reach close to the speed of light.

4. ( ) At a high velocity, crashing into even a tiny object could destroy a spacecraft.

5. ( ) Although worm holes may exist, it is very unlikely we could use them to cross space.

Listening Comprehension

🎧 19

Predict the correct questions for the answers below. Then check your responses with the audio.

1. _____

   It is about 40 trillion kilometers from Earth.

2. _____

   Yes, because they expel particles at a much higher speed than normal rockets.

3. _____

   Unfortunately, no. It does not seem like a realistic possibility.

Words in Science

Choose the correct word for each sentence from the list below.

1. If we _____ this part of the design, we may be able to make the machine more efficient.

2. Our design is still at a _____ stage, so it is difficult to estimate when we will be ready to manufacture it.

3. Electrons are negatively _____ particles.

4. A gasoline engine is still the _____ system for most automobiles at present.

5. Our entire _____ of rockets needs to change if we are to achieve high-velocity space travel.

concept	theoretical	charged	propulsion	alter

Understanding Technical Language – Giving Instructions

Place the following words into the sentences beneath the pictures.

| Insert | Measure | Calculate | Connect |
| Observe | Remove | Pour | Press |

1.

_____
the length of
the rectangle.

2.

_____
the liquid into
the beaker.

3.

_____
the wire to the
circuit.

4.

_____
the disk into
the drive.

5.

_____
the button to turn
on the machine.

6.

_____
your card from
the machine.

7.

_____
the value of x
in the equation.

8.

_____
the changes in
the sample.

Building Sentences – Comparing and Contrasting

Following the example given, rewrite the sentences below.

Ex: Interstellar travel is possible in theory. It is not realistic yet.

[Although]   *Although interstellar travel is possible in theory, it is not realistic yet.*

1. Ion engines are faster than rockets. They cannot approach light speed.

   [but] _____

2. It takes 7 months to reach Mars. Reaching a star would take 78,000 years.

   [while] _____

3. Planets near the Sun are very hot. Those far away are very cold.

   [whereas] _____

Discussion

Talk about these questions with your classmates.

1. Do you think that human beings will ever live on Mars? Would you like to go there, if it was possible?

2. Do you believe that intelligent aliens exist?

Unit 10: Limitless Energy

Nowadays there are many different ways to produce electricity, from fossil fuel plants to nuclear reactors. All of them, however, have limitations. Now engineers are experimenting with a new way to produce electricity. Could human beings one day enjoy limitless energy?

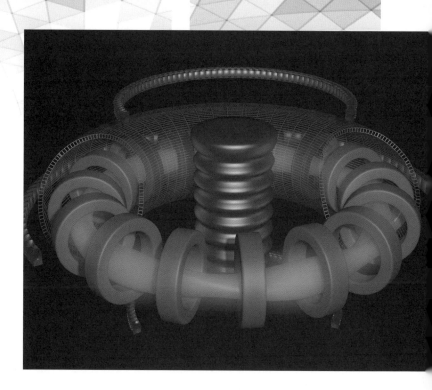

Key Vocabulary

Match the following words with their meaning.

1. interact   (a) to communicate with, react to

2. fossil fuel   (b) to be strong enough not to break

3. split   (c) a substance such as oil or coal

4. withstand   (d) to push something down with pressure

5. compress   (e) to divide into smaller parts

In many ways we are living in a world of science fiction. When science fiction writers of the past imagined the future, they pictured high-speed computers, mobile communication devices, automatic language translators, satellite networks, artificial intelligence, and robots that could speak and interact like humans. Most of these things have already been achieved, 5 or are on the way to being so. There is, however, one aspect of technology that has not caught up to science fiction. That is energy. Inspired by the early promise of nuclear power, science fiction writers imagined a world of limitless energy that could power flying cars and light-speed spaceships. This, sadly, is not the world we live in.

We do have a number of effective methods for generating energy, including the burning 10 of fossil fuels like oil or coal, the harnessing of solar, wind or wave energy, and the splitting of atoms to create nuclear power. However, there are limits to how much energy can be produced in these ways. For truly limitless energy, many scientists believe the future lies in a new version of nuclear power that involves not the splitting of atomic nuclei (called nuclear fission) but the bonding of them together, a process known as nuclear fusion. Nuclear fusion 15 is the energy that powers stars. The massive gravity within a star fuses together hydrogen nuclei to form helium. Our own Sun, for example, fuses 620 million cubic meters of hydrogen every second. The energy released in this process is far greater than that generated by nuclear fission.

The problem is that recreating the conditions inside the Sun in order to achieve nuclear 20 fusion here on Earth is a hugely difficult task. Lacking the gravitational pressure that exists within a star, engineers must use heat to force the hydrogen nuclei together, producing a temperature at least ten times higher than that of the Sun. Producing millions of degrees of heat, along with materials that can withstand it without breaking or melting, is an extremely complex task, and it has taken decades of hard work to even come close to achieving it. Now, 25 however, the dream of nuclear fusion is slowly getting closer. In Cadarache in southern France, an engineering project involving 34 different countries, including China and Japan, is constructing an experimental nuclear fusion reactor measuring 19 meters in diameter and 11 meters in height. The reactor works by compressing hot hydrogen plasma by means of a powerful electromagnet. It is safer than traditional nuclear power because, unlike with nuclear 30 fission, a nuclear fusion reaction can be stopped quickly in case of an accident or emergency.

The Cadarache reactor itself is not expected to produce very much energy, but, if the experiment is successful, it could point the way toward a future where the limitless energy dreamed of by science fiction writers finally becomes a reality.

(l. 5-6) catch up to ～に追いつく，足並みをそろえる　　(l. 10) harness ～を利用する，生かす　　(l. 13) nuclei 核（nucleus の複数形）　　(l. 13-14) nuclear fission 核分裂　　(l. 14) nuclear fusion 核融合 (l. 16) helium ヘリウム　　(l. 22) degrees 度（温度の単位）　　(l. 27) reactor 原子炉　　(l. 28) plasma プラズマ

Reading Comprehension

Decide if the following statements are true (T) or false (F).

1. (   ) Our current ability to generate energy is just like the world of science fiction.

2. (   ) Nuclear fusion involves dividing the nucleus of an atom to release energy.

3. (   ) Whereas stars use gravity to achieve nuclear fusion, on Earth we have to rely mainly on heat.

4. (   ) The temperature required to produce fusion is not as high as the Sun's.

5. (   ) Nuclear fusion should be a safer technology than nuclear fission.

Listening Comprehension

21

Predict the correct questions for the answers below. Then check your responses with the audio.

1. _____

   High-speed computers, mobile communication devices and satellite networks.

2. _____

   It is called nuclear fission.

3. _____

   It is 19 meters in diameter and 11 meters in height.

Words in Science

Choose the correct word for each sentence from the list below.

1. While fission means the splitting of atoms, _____ refers to the binding of them together.

2. The Sun burns at a temperature of almost 15 million _____ at its core.

3. _____ is a gas that is lighter than air.

4. Solar panels are a way to collect and _____ the energy of the Sun.

5. Nuclear fusion may help us to _____ the world of science fiction.

fusion	helium	degrees	harness	catch up to

Understanding Technical Language – Graphs and Figures I

Match the following words with the pictures below.

> pie chart   flow chart   bar graph   line graph
> bullet points   diagram   table   scatter plot

1.

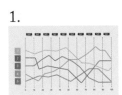

_____

2.

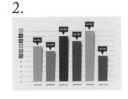

_____

3.

_____

4.

_____

5.

_____

6.

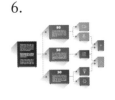

_____

7.

_____

8.

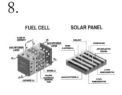

_____

Building Sentences – Comparisons with Adjectives

Put the words in the correct order and rewrite the sentences below.

Ex: Nuclear (safer / fusion / than / is / technology / a) nuclear fission.

     Nuclear *fusion is a safer technology than* nuclear fission.

1. It is (nuclear / more / than / difficult / to / much / achieve / fusion) fission.

_____

2. Generating solar energy (expensive / is / as / used / as / not / it) to be.

_____

3. The energy released by fusion (is / that / greater / than / by / generated) fission.

_____

Discussion

Talk about these questions with your classmates.

1. Imagine the world in the year 2100. What do you think the main ways to generate electricity will be (e.g. fossil fuel, solar, nuclear etc.)?

2. If we had access to limitless energy, how do you think the world would change?

Unit 11: The Surprising Uses of Nanotechnology

Nanotechnology is the science of creating materials that are almost as small as atoms. Although it sounds like a technology of the future, it is actually used in many everyday items, including baseball bats, tennis balls, clothing and skincare products.

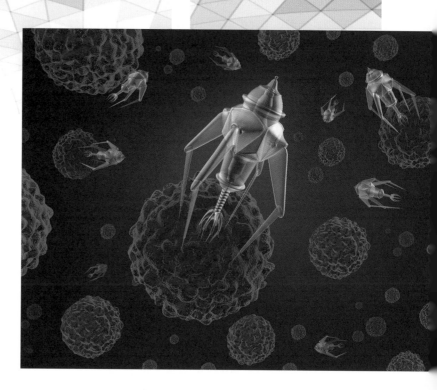

Key Vocabulary

Match the following words with their meaning.

1. application   (a) very small organisms that sometimes cause disease

2. manufacture   (b) the making of goods or products

3. bacteria   (c) medical treatment which involves cutting into the body

4. shrink   (d) a way in which something can be used

5. surgical operation   (e) to make something smaller

A nanometer is a billionth of a meter. To help you understand how small this is, the diameter of a human hair is about 80,000 nanometers and the thickness of a sheet of paper is 100,000 nanometers. Human DNA is 2.5 nanometers, in diameter, while atoms range in size from 0.1 to 0.5 nanometers. Nanotechnology is the science of creating materials, components and
5 machines at this tiny scale.

There are countless applications for nanotechnology, some that are already in use today and others that are expected in the near future. You may be surprised at how common some of these applications are. For instance, one advantage of using nanotechnology is that you can make materials stronger and more durable without adding any extra weight. For this purpose,
10 nanoparticles are often used in the manufacture of baseball bats, tennis rackets, bicycles, motorcycle helmets, cars, trucks and airplanes. Nanoparticles can also improve the performance of golf clubs and even reduce the speed at which air leaks out from a tennis ball. In the fashion industry, special nanotech coatings have been created to make clothes water-resistant or stain proof. Other coatings kill bacteria to stop unpleasant smells or block
15 ultraviolet rays to protect the wearer from sunburn. Nanoparticles are also used in skincare products to deliver vitamins deeper into the skin.

The chances are, then, that you have already used products which make use of nanotechnology. But how about applications beyond such everyday items? In electronics, nanotechnology has been used to shrink the size of transistors within computer chips in order
20 to make them smaller and more powerful. In 2000, a typical transistor was between 130 and 250 nanometers in size; in 2016, a laboratory in California demonstrated the first 1-nanometer transistor. More efficient transistors may eventually mean that your computer's entire memory could be stored on just one tiny chip. In the same field, nanomaterials could also be used to create flexible electronic devices, such as electronic paper that can be rolled up
25 and wearable solar generators that charge your smartphone as you walk.

The most exciting applications for nanotechnology come in the field of medicine. Nanotechnology is already being used to treat certain kinds of cancer through the use of lasers which apply heat to nanoparticles placed inside the unhealthy cells. There is also the prospect of creating microscopic nanorobots that could be sent into the bloodstream to carry
30 out delicate surgical operations inside the body. Finally, there may also be good news for those who hate getting their influenza injection each year. Scientists are currently working on ways to use nanotechnology to deliver vaccines without the use of a needle.

(l. 3) range 及ぶ　　(l. 6) countless 無数の　　(l. 9) durable 耐久性のある，丈夫な　　(l. 13) coating 塗装，コーティング　　(l. 14) stain proof 防汚，汚れを弾く　　(l. 19) transistor トランジスタ　　(l. 24) flexible 柔軟性のある，曲げやすい　　(l. 29) prospect 見通し，可能性　　(l. 31) injection 注射

Reading Comprehension

Decide if the following statements are true (T) or false (F).

1. (   ) Human DNA is smaller than an atom.

2. (   ) Nanoparticles can help to strengthen baseball bats and tennis rackets.

3. (   ) Raincoats might be one item of clothing likely to make use of nanotechnology.

4. (   ) In 2016, a transistor was created that was over 100 times smaller than one from 2000.

5. (   ) Nanorobots can now carry out surgical operations inside the human body.

Listening Comprehension

23

Predict the correct questions for the answers below. Then check your responses with the audio.

1. _____
   Around 100,000 nanometers.

2. _____
   It stops unpleasant smells.

3. _____
   Electronic paper that can be rolled up.

Words in Science

Choose the correct word for each sentence from the list below.

1. A special _____ was put on the material to make it resistant to water.

2. Vaccines are usually given by _____ .

3. The more _____ a material is, the longer it will last.

4. The chip uses a new, very small type of _____ .

5. The applications of nanotechnology _____ from medicine to clothing.

transistor	coating	durable	range	injection

Understanding Technical Language – Graphs and Figures II

pie chart	flow chart	bar graph	line graph
bullet points	diagram	table	scatter plot

1. Trends over time:

   _____

2. A process:

   _____

3. Percentages:

   _____

4. A list of points:

   _____

5. Ranking:

   _____

6. Specific facts or numbers:

   _____

7. The main features of something:

   _____

8. The relationship between two sets of data:

   _____

Building Sentences – Expressing Purpose

Following the example given, rewrite the sentences below.

Ex: Nanomaterials could also be used. (Creating) flexible electronic devices.

    [to] Nanomaterials could also be used *to create* flexible electronic devices.

1. Engineers shrink the size of transistors. (Making) chips more powerful.

   [in order to] _____

2. Nanoparticles are added to baseball bats. (Increasing) their strength.

   [so as to] _____

3. The researchers will work through the night. (Finish) the experiment.

   [so that] _____

Discussion

Talk about these questions with your classmates.

1. Which of the products which make use of nanotechnology have you experienced or used?

2. What electronic devices do you wish could be made smaller or more powerful? Why?

Unit 12: Creating the Perfect Human

In 2018, the world was shocked when the first genetically modified babies were born in China. The illegal experiment raised the possibility of creating 'designer babies' who are stronger and smarter than other human beings. What effect will this have on the world?

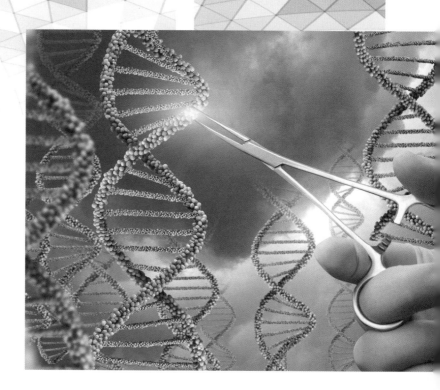

Key Vocabulary

Match the following words with their meaning.

1. modify   (a) to change, alter

2. consequence   (b) on purpose, planned

3. critic   (c) a result, effect

4. deliberate   (d) related to what is right or wrong

5. ethical   (e) a person who says they do not support something

In 2018, a doctor in China by the name of He Jiankui shocked the scientific community when he announced he had successfully altered the genes of twin baby girls to prevent them from contracting the HIV virus which causes AIDS. The doctor, who appeared to have acted without the knowledge or permission of the Chinese government, changed the girls' DNA
5 while they were still embryos in the womb, modifying a gene known as CCR5 to make the girls resistant to HIV. The two girls were born in hospital without any major problems, the world's first examples of genetically edited babies.

In most countries of the world, including China, gene editing on human beings is illegal. While Dr. He defended the work, saying that the girls' parents volunteered for the
10 experiment, the reaction of the global community was extremely critical. Scientists pointed out that there may be long-term negative consequences to altering gene CCR5 that we do not know about, perhaps shortening the girls' lifespans. Other critics objected to the principle of the experiment, arguing that it opened the way to the creation of so-called 'designer babies,' which could change human society forever.

15 A designer baby is one whose genes have been deliberately modified to improve it in some way. While Dr. He's experiment is the only known instance of genetic modification being carried out on a human baby, it has been done on animals (and plants) for a number of years. Genetically modified mice, pigs and goats have been used in laboratories to produce drugs for human diseases, including an anticoagulant drug which was extracted from goat's
20 milk. Cows and sheep have also been genetically engineered to make them grow faster, stronger and healthier.

Such research is largely accepted within the scientific world. The use of genetic modification on humans, on the other hand, is far more controversial. Dr. He's research was aimed at increasing the babies' resistance to a particular disease, which is the most likely first
25 step toward designer babies. However, there is no technological reason why babies could not be "improved" in other ways. Would you like your child to grow up to be taller than average? To have different colored eyes or hair? To be blessed with healthy white teeth? To be more intelligent than other people? All of these traits are, to some extent, related to genes, and could, therefore, be modifiable through genetic engineering. The potential arrival of designer
30 babies raises the possibility of a race of superhumans, who are faster, stronger and more intelligent than everyone else. Would this be a good thing for the world?

The speed of scientific advances brings up serious ethical issues that have to be discussed on a global scale. Genetic engineering is certainly one of the most important.

(l. 2) gene 遺伝子　　(l. 3) contract 〜に感染する，病気にかかる　　(l. 5) embryo 胚，胎芽　　(l. 5) womb 子宮　　(l. 8) illegal 違法の　　(l. 12) lifespan 寿命　　(l. 19) anticoagulant (血液の) 凝固を防ぐ，抗凝固　　(l. 19) extract 〜を抽出する　　(l. 28) trait 特徴，特質

Reading Comprehension

Decide if the following statements are true (T) or false (F).

1. (   ) The world's first genetically edited babies were born in China in 2018.

2. (   ) Dr. He's work was supported by the Chinese government.

3. (   ) We do not know what the long-term effects of Dr. He's experiment may be.

4. (   ) Genetic engineering of animals and plants is not so controversial.

5. (   ) Genetic modification could lead to humans who are taller and more intelligent than average.

Listening Comprehension

25

Predict the correct questions for the answers below. Then check your responses with the audio.

1. _____

   It is called CCR5.

2. _____

   Because they were worried it would lead to the creation of 'designer babies.'

3. _____

   Because the spread of scientific advances can affect the whole world.

Words in Science

Choose the correct word for each sentence from the list below.

1. Modifying the _____ of animals and plants is not uncommon.

2. The _____ of an elephant is longer than that of a mouse.

3. We inherit _____ like eye color, hair color and height from our parents.

4. Most people think that genetic modification of human babies should be _____ .

5. Long ago, human beings learned how to _____ salt from sea water.

> lifespan   extract   illegal   traits   genes

Understanding Technical Language – Numbers and Graphs

① *Write the following in numbers.*

1. 10 thousand   _____
2. 1 hundred thousand   _____

3. 1 million   _____
4. 1 billion   _____

5. 12 thousand 4 hundred   _____
6. 256 thousand   _____

7. 1.7 million   _____
8. 2.8 billion   _____

② *Match the following terms to the graph.*

mean	mode	x-axis	y-axis	distribution curve

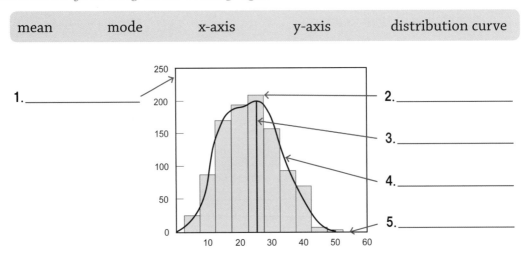

1._____

2._____

3._____

4._____

5._____

Building Sentences – Verbs with Prepositions

Put the words in the correct order and rewrite the sentences below.

Ex: Dr. He altered the genes of babies (contracting / prevent / to / them / HIV / from / the) virus.

Dr. He altered the genes of babies *to prevent them from contracting the HIV* virus.

1. His (aimed / is / at / research / babies' / increasing / the) resistance to a disease.

_____

2. The (people / to / project / objected / by / was / many) on account of its cost.

_____

3. The (an / had / for / student / to / important / prepare) exam.

_____

Discussion

Talk about these questions with your classmates.

1. What do you think about Dr. He's work?

2. Do you think that creating designer babies should be illegal in Japan? Why?

Unit 13: The New Age of Computing

Computers have become more and more powerful over the past three decades. But some scientists believe we are reaching the limit. What kind of technology will the new generation of computers use?

Key Vocabulary

Match the following words with their meaning.

1. turn out   (a) usual or normal

2. branch   (b) to become, have a particular result

3. conventional   (c) at the same time

4. store   (d) to keep or collect

5. simultaneously   (e) a field or aspect (of a science)

Back in the 1960s, the founder of the technology company Intel, Gordon Moore, predicted that the power of computers would double every eighteen months. Known as Moore's Law, this prediction has generally turned out to be correct. In fact, there is more computing power in a modern smart phone than there was in the fastest supercomputers of the 1990s. The reason for this dramatic increase in power is our ability to create smaller and smaller transistors, the fundamental components of computer chips. The most powerful chips today can contain as many as 30 billion transistors, each not much larger than a nanometer.

Some scientists believe, however, that we are reaching the limit of how small transistors can become. To make the next leap in computing power, they are turning to a new kind of technology known as quantum computing. Quantum theory is the branch of physics that deals with atoms and particles, and the idea of quantum computing is to make use of this strange world to create chips that could work millions of times faster than the ones we use today.

To understand how quantum computing works, we first have to understand how conventional computers operate. A computer stores all its data in the form of a code based on binary numbers, either 1 or 0. So a capital 'A', for example, is stored as 1000001 and a small 'a' as 01100001. Transistors provide the means by which computers manipulate these numbers. A transistor can either be on or off, like a light switch in your home. If it is on, it stores a number 1; if it is off, it stores a 0. A computer performs calculations by processing these numbers step by step, following a particular list of instructions called an algorithm. The more transistors a computer has, the quicker it can do this.

The precise mechanism of a quantum computer is too complex to describe here, but the most important thing to understand is that, unlike a conventional transistor, a quantum transistor (one that is smaller than an atom) could store both a 1 and a 0 *at the same time*. Moreover, it wouldn't have to calculate in a series of steps but could do multiple calculations simultaneously. The reason why this would be possible is due to the dual nature of atomic particles, which behave as both particles and waves. They are, in effect, two things at the same time—like a 1 and a 0. If we can harness this phenomenon, we can use it to create a completely new kind of computer chip.

If this sounds complicated, that's because it is. Scientists have been studying the idea of quantum computing for 30 years, and we are still not there yet. However, some of the biggest companies in the world, including Google and Microsoft, are researching the problem seriously, and it seems likely that sometime in the next few decades, the first practical quantum computer will be built.

(l. 1) founder 創設者　　(l. 10) quantum 量子　　(l. 15) binary 2 進法の，2 値の
(l. 16) manipulate ～を処理する，操作する　　(l. 25) dual 二つから構成される，二面性がある
(l. 27) phenomenon 現象

Reading Comprehension

Decide if the following statements are true (T) or false (F).

1. (   ) Moore's Law predicts that computers will get more powerful as time goes by.
2. (   ) There may be a limit to how powerful conventional computers can become.
3. (   ) Conventional computers carry out calculations as a step by step process.
4. (   ) A quantum transistor would be able to store either a 1 or a 0, but not both.
5. (   ) A practical quantum computer has recently been built by Google.

Listening Comprehension   27

Predict the correct questions for the answers below. Then check your responses with the audio.

1. _____
   As many as 30 billion.

2. _____
   It is called quantum theory.

3. _____
   They behave as both particles and waves.

Words in Science

Choose the correct word for each sentence from the list below.

1. A _____ system is composed of two units or parts.
2. The _____ that Google uses for its search engine was developed by Sergey Brin and Larry Page.
3. Konosuke Matsushita, the _____ of Panasonic, is often called 'the god of management.'
4. The _____ world is mysterious and hard to understand.
5. Computers are very good at _____ numbers in order to perform calculations.

> algorithm   manipulating   quantum   founder   binary

Understanding Technical Language – Describing Functions

① *Match the following words with the pictures below.*

| thermometer | battery | wire | antenna | safety goggles |

1.
2.
3.
4.
5.

_____   _____   _____   _____   _____

② *Match the equipment or component with its function.*

1. The function of a thermometer is
2. A battery is used
3. The function of a wire is
4. Safety goggles are used
5. The function of an antenna is

a) to supply electrical power to a circuit.
b) to receive radio signals.
c) to measure the temperature of a material.
d) to protect the wearer's eyes from damage.
e) to conduct electricity around a circuit.

Building Sentences – Expressing Probabilities

Following the example given, rewrite the sentences below.

Ex: The first practical quantum computer will be built.

[likely] It is *likely* that the first practical quantum computer will be built.

1. He will succeed in his research.

[sure to] He _____

2. They will make even smaller transistors.

[likely] It _____

3. Human beings will one day live on Mars.

[possibility] There _____

Discussion

Talk about these questions with your classmates.

1. Do you enjoy using computers? What do you use them for?
2. If quantum computers could be made, what do you think they would be used for?

Unit 14: The Coming of the Machines

The rise of artificial intelligence means that in the near future, robots and computers may take over many of the jobs currently done by human beings. What effect will this have on society and will it be a good or a bad thing?

Key Vocabulary

Match the following words with their meaning.

1. occupation   (a) controlled or performed by machines

2. automation   (b) related to how people think and learn

3. cognitive   (c) to buy

4. evolve   (d) to develop gradually

5. purchase   (e) a job or profession

In 2013, researchers at Oxford University published a report entitled *The Future of Employment*, which predicted that over the next twenty years more than half of occupations could disappear due to automation. Analyzing 702 current jobs, the team found that as many as 404 of them were likely to be taken over by robots or computers. These jobs included not
5 only low-skilled work, such as manufacturing, driving and fast food cooking, but also the high-skilled work of lawyers, accountants, financial analysts and journalists. The study predicted that 95 percent of accounting tasks and much of the day-to-day work of lawyers would soon be performed by computers.

The reason for the study's dramatic prediction was the rise of artificial intelligence.
10 Artificial intelligence (AI) is the ability of computers to demonstrate cognitive functions that we associate with human minds, including learning, problem solving and speech. The Oxford University study was based on the assumption that the more AI advanced, the more human tasks it would be able to perform. Is this really likely to happen? The short answer is: yes, eventually. Although not all experts agree on how fast or how deep AI's impact on the labor
15 market will be, there is little doubt there are big changes ahead. The McKinsey Global Institute recently predicted that up to one-third of American workers will have to find a new occupation by 2030. The thinking about the progress of AI can be summed up in the following way: AI can probably do less than you think right now, but it will eventually do more than you think, in more areas of life, and will evolve faster than technologies have in the past.

20 Will this be a good thing for society on the whole? That is a difficult question to answer. Big technological advances in the past, such as the Industrial Revolution of the 19th century or the IT Revolution of the 20th century, produced new kinds of jobs that replaced those lost to automation. This may happen with the AI Revolution; however, as many experts have pointed out, there is no guarantee this will be the case. A more positive view is that, as more
25 things are designed and manufactured by machines, the cheaper they will become to purchase. As a result, in the future we may be able to live without as much money as today, enabling us to work less hard. In 1930, the economist John Maynard Keynes forecast that within a century advances in technology would mean that the working week was reduced to just fifteen hours, with the rest of the time available for leisure and play. Some people were hoping that the IT
30 Revolution would deliver this future during the 1990s. It did not, but the AI Revolution perhaps offers more hope. In the meantime, we will need to be flexible in our thinking and willing to learn new skills in order to keep ourselves one step ahead of the machines.

(l. 4) take over ～を引き継ぐ, 奪う   (l. 11) associate with (～で～を) 連想する   (l. 12)
assumption 前提, 想定   (l. 14-15) labor market 労働市場   (l. 17) sum up 要約する, まとめる
(l. 26) enable ～を可能にする   (l. 27) forecast ～を予想する, 予測する

Reading Comprehension

Decide if the following statements are true (T) or false (F).

1. (   ) Automation will affect low-skilled but not high-skilled occupations.
2. (   ) Experts know exactly how the labor market will be impacted by the rise of AI.
3. (   ) AI may do less than you expect now, but in the future it will probably do more.
4. (   ) During two previous technological revolutions, new jobs were created to replace the ones that were lost.
5. (   ) The prediction of John Maynard Keynes may come true thanks to the AI Revolution.

Listening Comprehension

29

Predict the correct questions for the answers below. Then check your responses with the audio.

1. _____

   It was called *The Future of Employment*.

2. _____

   Learning, problem solving and speech.

3. _____

   No, unfortunately it did not.

Words in Science

Choose the correct word for each sentence from the list below.

1. It is likely that computers will _____ human jobs in the near future.
2. At the end of the class, I will _____ the main points of the lecture.
3. The writers of the report made the _____ that AI will continue to progress.
4. One aspect of human behavior we do not _____ with machines is emotion.
5. The rise of AI could _____ us to have more time for leisure and play.

| assumption | enable | sum up | take over | associate |

61

Understanding Technical Language – Fields of Science and Engineering

Match the field of science and engineering with the description on the right.

1. Physics
2. Chemistry
3. Biology
4. Mechanical engineering
5. Electrical and electronic engineering
6. Civil engineering
7. Materials science
8. Marine science
9. Computer science
10. Aeronautical engineering

a) deals with the design and analysis of aircraft.
b) is concerned with the construction of bridges, dams and roads.
c) involves the study of oceans and sea life.
d) deals with software and hardware design.
e) is concerned with the nature and properties of matter and energy.
f) involves the design of electrical systems.
g) deals with the study of living organisms.
h) is concerned with substances used in manufacturing.
i) involves the manufacture of machines and engines.
j) deals with the properties and reactions of matter.

Building Sentences – Expressions with Numbers

Put the words in the correct order and rewrite the sentences below.

Ex: The team found that (as / of / 404 / as / the / many / jobs) were likely to be taken over.
    The team found that *as many as 404 of the jobs* were likely to be taken over.

1. The report suggested that (workers / to / 35 / of / percent / American / up) would have to find a new occupation.

   _____

2. Based on its new technology, the company was able to (dollars / much / make / million / as / 40 / in / as) profit.

   _____

3. We should (of / than / fewer / 10,000 / no / these / sell) new cars this year.

   _____

Discussion

Talk about these questions with your classmates.

1. What job would you like to have in the future? Will it be affected by the rise of AI?
2. Do you think the AI Revolution will be a positive or negative thing for society?

Unit 15: The Future of Medicine

Like other advanced countries, Japan is facing the problem of an aging society. Could advances in medicine help to solve these issues? Let's look at how medical care is likely to evolve in the coming decades.

🗩 Key Vocabulary

Match the following words with their meaning.

1. benefit   (a) very important

2. figure   (b) something that produces a good result

3. vital   (c) to help

4. monitor   (d) a number

5. assist   (e) to watch or observe for a particular purpose

The advance of medical technology over the past hundred years has been one of the greatest achievements of the human race, allowing us to live longer and healthier than ever before. We have already seen in this book the benefits that nanotechnology might bring to medicine in the future, as well as the possibilities (and risks) that come with the technology of genetic
5 modification. But in what other ways is medicine likely to change over the coming years?

One of the biggest challenges facing the world, and Japan in particular, is the prospect of an aging society. Currently around 28 percent of Japan's population is aged over 65, with this figure expected to rise to almost 40 percent by 2050. In terms of medical care, this will lead to several major problems, including a shortage of doctors, nurses and carers and a lack of
10 workers able to pay the taxes required to keep the healthcare system functioning. It is vital, therefore, for Japan to develop new, efficient forms of medicine that can deal with these issues.

Fortunately, however, there is hope. Recent years have seen the rise of wearable technologies like the Fitbit which can measure and record fitness activities. In the near future, these sensing technologies are likely to include healthcare functions, enabling the continuous
15 monitoring of heart rates, breathing patterns, blood pressure and blood sugar. Other sensors may be able to pick up early signs of cancer and other diseases. The data from these sensors will be transmitted via Bluetooth to computers which, aided by artificial intelligence, could help to diagnose illnesses and suggest treatments. Doctors will, of course, still be necessary. However, by providing them with continuous data about a patient's health condition, it may
20 not be necessary to visit them in person. This will save people from long waits at hospitals and enable fewer doctors to treat larger numbers of patients.

Another technological development is the rise of robots to assist elderly or disabled people in their daily lives. There are two main types: companion robots and assistive robots. Companion robots, such as Softbank's Pepper, will grow more advanced in the coming years,
25 offering conversation and basic help for elderly people living alone at home. Assistive robots will be able to carry out more physical functions, such as lifting heavy objects, helping people to get up from beds and chairs, and even preparing and serving meals. Another useful technology is the so-called 'bionic suit,' a mechanical device worn on the body which amplifies the wearer's strength. Such suits are already being used in rehabilitation clinics to
30 help people who have lost the use of their limbs through accident or illness.

While care robots are still rather basic, Japan is leading the way in research and will continue to make advances. Whether they will be enough to solve the problems of an aging society remains to be seen, but technology could be our best hope for the future.

(l. 6) prospect 見通し，可能性　(l. 14) sensing technology 検出技術　(l. 17) transmit ～を送信する　(l. 17) aid 補助する　(l. 28) bionic 人工の，バイオニック　(l. 29) amplify ～を増強する (l. 30) limb 手足

Reading Comprehension

Decide if the following statements are true (T) or false (F).

1. (   ) One problem of an aging society is a lack of workers to pay for the healthcare system.

2. (   ) The Fitbit is a device that measures blood pressure and blood sugar.

3. (   ) Thanks to wearable technologies, doctors will not be needed in the future.

4. (   ) Softbank's Pepper is an example of an assistive robot that should be able to lift elderly people out of bed.

5. (   ) Bionic suits are currently being used for rehabilitation purposes.

Listening Comprehension

31

Predict the correct questions for the answers below. Then check your responses with the audio.

1. _____

   Almost 40 percent.

2. _____

   For example, the monitoring of heart rates, breathing patterns, blood pressure and blood sugar.

3. _____

   Companion robots and assistive robots.

Words in Science

Choose the correct word for each sentence from the list below.

1. Having lost the use of a _____ in an accident, the young man began a long period of rehabilitation.

2. Bluetooth is a technology which can _____ data from one device to another.

3. The function of a speaker is to _____ sound in a room.

4. The _____ of an aging society is less worrying if we consider the future benefits of technology.

5. Due to a _____ of doctors, the patients had to wait a long time for treatment.

> shortage   transmit   prospect   amplify   limb

Understanding Technical Language – Jobs in Science and Engineering

Match the job with the description on the right.

1. A geoscientist   a) performs tasks to assist with experiments and research.
2. A surveyor   b) finds ways to extract oil and gas from the Earth.
3. A lab technician   c) deals with money issues in various kinds of organizations.
4. A security analyst   d) studies the physical aspects of the Earth.
5. A cost estimator   e) prepares medicines for patients.
6. A financial analyst   f) predicts the time and money needed for projects.
7. A biochemist   g) monitors and protects computer networks.
8. A petroleum engineer   h) provides detailed analyses of numerical data.
9. A statistician   i) carries out research in healthcare and other fields.
10. A pharmacist   j) makes exact measurements for land development.

Building Sentences – Giving Examples

Put the words in the correct order and rewrite the sentences below.

Ex: An aging society will lead to several problems, (a / doctors / to / shortage / of / treat / including) patients.

An aging society will lead to several problems, *including a shortage of doctors to treat* patients.

1. The new robot can carry out various functions, (helping / as / out / an / elderly / such / person / get) of bed.

   _____

2. Technology may be able to solve many problems, (the / society / those / by / caused / aging / of / including).

   _____

3. Global temperatures are increasing due to the (carbon / like / emission / gases / into / dioxide / of) the atmosphere.

   _____

Discussion

Talk about these questions with your classmates.

1. Are you worried about Japan's aging society? Why / why not?

2. What other problems does the world face? Do you think technology could solve them?

Key Vocabulary

【A】

accelerate

activate

act on

algebra

algorithm

alter

amplify

application

aspect

assist

associate

assume

assumption

astronomy

automation

【B】

bacteria

benefit

best case scenario

binary

branch

【C】

catch up to

charged

cognitive

collide (with)

come up with

comparatively

component

comprehend

compress

comprised of

concept

conduct

consequence

consistent with

contradict

controversial

conventional

copper

【D】

decimal

deduce

degree(s)

deliberate

detect

determine

diagnose

division

dominant

【E】

electrode

electrolyte

electromagnetism

electron

element

emit

emphasize

enable

encounter

eradicate

ethical

evolve

exist

expel

explore

exposure

extract

【F】

facilitate

figure

figure out

founder

force

fossil fuel

fraction

frequency

fundamental

【G】

gene

geometry

gravity

【H】

harness

helium

hypothesis

【I】

illegal

immunity

infectious disease

infrared

interact

【L】

life expectancy

lifespan

【M】

manipulate

manufacture

matter

measles

model

modify

monitor

motion

multiplication

【N】

nuclear fission

nuclear fusion

nucleus

【O】

observation

occupation

orbit

organism

【P】

particle

phenomenon

precise

predict

principle

probability

property

propose

propulsion

prospect

purchase

【Q】

quantum

【R】

radioactive

refract

【S】

scholar

seismic

semiconductor

sequence

shortage

shrink

simultaneously

split

store

sum up

surgical operation

【T】

take over

theorem

theoretical

theory

trait

transmit

trend

【U】

ultrasound

【V】

velocity

verify

vital

【W】

withstand

Advances in Science [B-899]

Learning from the Past, Looking to the Future

私たちと科学の世界―過去から未来へ

1 刷	2020 年 4 月 1 日
4 刷	2023 年 8 月 30 日

著　者	デイブ・リア　　Dave Rear
	村上　嘉代子　　Kayoko Murakami

発行者　南雲　一範　Kazunori Nagumo
発行所　株式会社　南雲堂
　　　　〒162-0801　東京都新宿区山吹町 361
　　　　NAN'UN-DO CO.,Ltd.
　　　　361 Yamabuki-cho, Shinjuku-ku, Tokyo 162-0801, Japan
　　　　振替口座：00160-0-46863
　　　　TEL：03-3268-2311(営業部：学校関係)
　　　　　　　03-3268-2384(営業部：書店関係)
　　　　　　　03-3268-2387(編集部)
　　　　FAX：03-3269-2486

編集者	伊藤　宏実
イラスト	Yasco Sudaka
製　版	日本ハイコム株式会社
装　丁	NONdesign
検　印	省　略
コード	ISBN 978-4-523-17899-6　　　C0082

Printed in Japan

E-mail　nanundo@post.email.ne.jp
URL　　https://www.nanun-do.co.jp/